missa tiburtina

giles swayne

NOVELLO PUBLISHING LIMITED

Order no: NOV 072498

missa tiburtina was commissioned in 1985 by the International Kodály Society, and first performed at The Queen Elizabeth Hall, London, on July 21st 1985 by the International Kodaly Youth Choir, conducted by John Poole. At this stage there were only five movements. The Gloria was added in the following year, and the complete work was first performed on August 1st 1986 at St. Luke's, Chelsea, as part of the 1986 Proms. The BBC Singers were conducted by Giles Swayne. Since then the work has had many performances all over the world. Various collections and revisions have been made for this new edition.

Duration about 24 minutes

The verses preceding the movements are by the composer and are © copyright 1990 Novello & Co. Ltd. Permission to reproduce the verses and the composer's preface must be obtained from the publisher.

Music typeset by New Notations London

Novello & Co. Ltd. welcomes information about performances of this work: details should be sent to the Performance Promotion Department

missa tiburtina

giles swayne

(1985)

Every year the world spends $750 billion on weapons
Every year 40 million people die (directly or indirectly) of hunger
Every year the UK alone spends over £200 million on slimming foods
Every sixty seconds 30 children die (directly or indirectly) of hunger
One quarter of all food in the USA is thrown away uneaten
10% of all living species (including plants) are under threat of extinction by the year 2000 **

** these figures are taken from *The Gaia Atlas of Planet Management*, published in 1985 by Pan Books

The rich nations of the world, out of greed, insecurity and muddle, are starving the poor nations, destroying the genetic heritage which is the foundation of our planet's future, and wasting its resources at a rate which is scarcely credible. In our age of unbelief we look to man to solve our problems, but this problem is vast, intractable, and self-imposed; man seems to have neither the ability nor the will to tackle it.

That is the background to this piece. It is a prayer for sanity, a cry in the wilderness to a god who may or may not be there. It is emphatically **not** a conventionally Christian piece: To my mind (and this means no disrespect to the faith of those who sincerely believe) Christianity lost the way, the truth and the life when it became a self-justifying institution (or rather a number of institutions, all squabbling with each other). Too much blood has been spilt, too many books burnt or locked away. But the form of the Mass allows many interpretations. This Mass is angrily critical of the intolerance, injustice and corruption of our world and those who control it. Some may find this blasphemous. Christ, I think, would have heartily approved. Its message is not so very different from what he was saying about Judaism, nearly two thousand years ago.

missa tiburtina was begun in Tivoli, near Rome. The title derives from the Latin name for Tivoli (Tibur). It is dedicated to my wife Naa Otuá, who comes from the so-called Third World and understands the meaning of poverty. While singing it, or listening to it, it is worth reflecting that in the course of its twenty minutes, six hundred children will have died – directly or indirectly – of starvation. This starvation is the inevitable consequence of our own prosperity. That is the real blasphemy.

giles swayne

May 1989

I: kyrie eleison   1

II: gloria   7

III: sanctus   12

IV: benedictus   16

V: agnus dei   25

VI: dona nobis pacem   28

kyrie eleison

The poor

have no voice.

They grow weaker daily

while we gobble up the goodies.

We are the fat boy of the class

who makes himself sick

on too much cake.

Here and now

a poor people

calls upon its god.

They have little hope

their cry will be answered.

They are the disinherited

of our sweet planet,

Earth.

·

missa tiburtina

I: kyrie

giles swayne

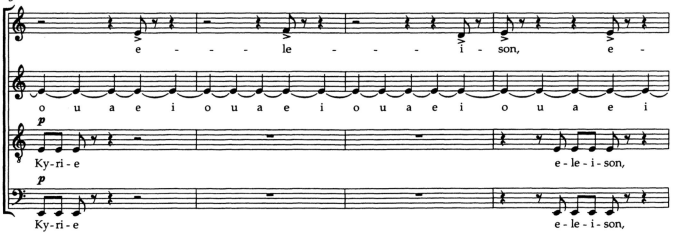

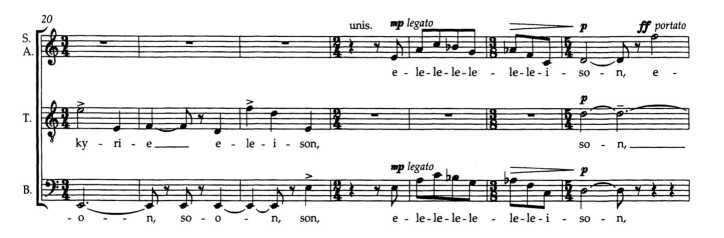

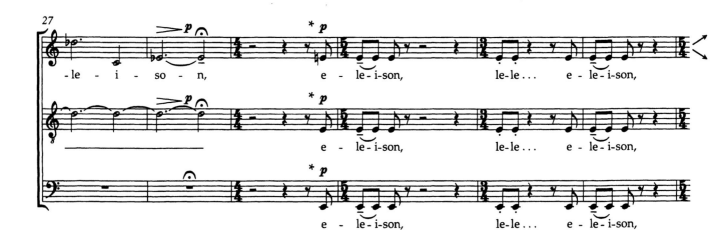

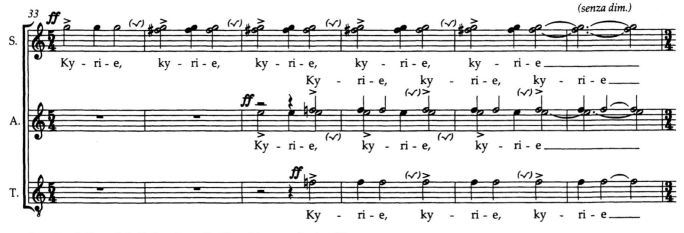

* muttered, through half-closed mouths. Revert to normal at bar 33.

* muttered, through half-closed mouths. Revert to normal at bar 52.

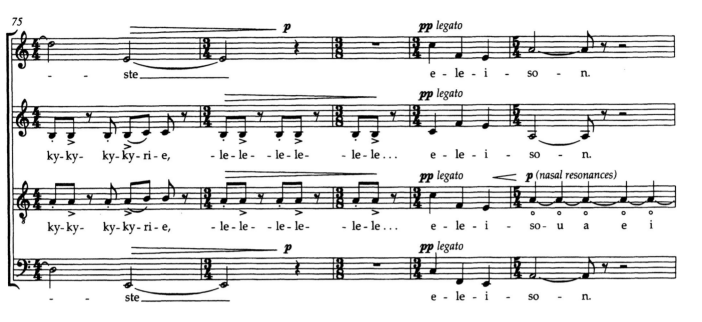

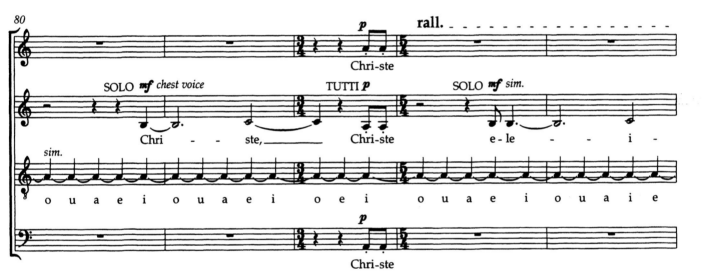

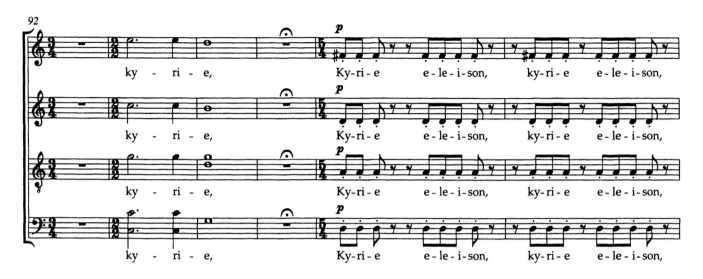

ky - ri - e, Kyri-e e-le-i-son, ky-ri-e e-le-i-son,

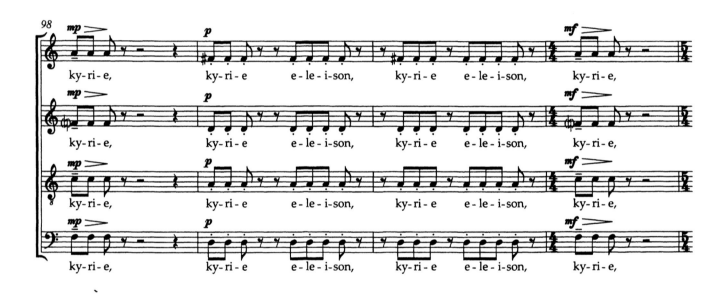

ky-ri-e, ky-ri-e e-le-i-son, ky-ri-e e-le-i-son, ky-ri-e,

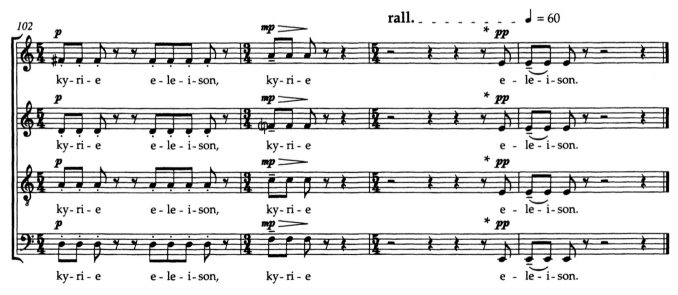

ky-ri-e e-le-i-son, ky-ri-e e-le-i-son.

* murmured: lips half-closed.

gloria

Voodoo.

To destroy

a people's beliefs

is as terrible as

destroying a rain-forest:

kinder to kill them.

(for Christ's sake)

Like zombies,

these people mutter,

stammer a sullen monotone.

We hear their secret thoughts:

glory . . . peace . . . have mercy on us . . .

Jesus Christ . . .

(more a curse than a prayer)

The *amen* screams rebellion,

but collapses,

defeated.

The odds

are too

great.

•

II: gloria

* Basses on low E ♯ until bar 50

* Semichorus: 4 voices on each line
(i.e. add 3 voices to each solo line)

* low basses: up to

semichorus: rejoin tutti unison

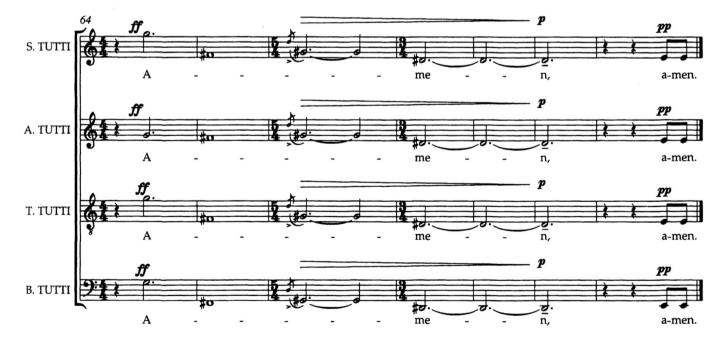

sanctus	benedictus

The wonders

of heaven and earth –

yippee in excelsis!

The earth-god is dying,

poisoned by lil' old us.

His sunshade is tattered and torn,

his forest lungs shrink daily, daily –

the people who lived in their shade

are hunted down like animals.

(sorry – we never realised . . .)

And all because

the great white god,

Mammon,

and Profit, his prophet,

have decreed that Greed

makes the world go round.

But

unless we learn

to live and let live,

we shall be left

with nothing.

(all of us)

Zero.

•

Work-songs, play-songs . . .

Against all odds,

the poor find happiness:

sweeter because it is not bought.

Their laughter is guiltless:

they have enslaved no-one,

polluted nothing,

dreamed up no Armageddon

for their grandchildren.

We rich

have gained the world,

but lost our souls.

I tell you,

the man is right:

no camel will fit

through a needle's

eye.

•

14

III: sanctus

Steady [♩ = 66]

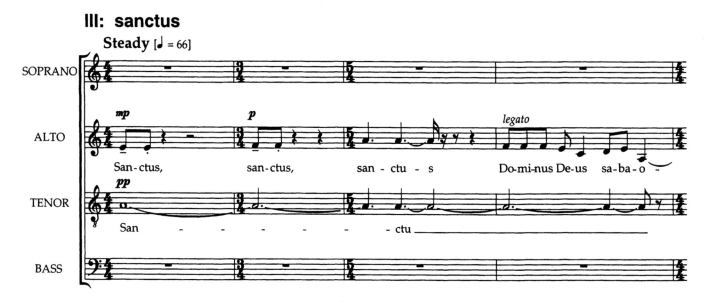

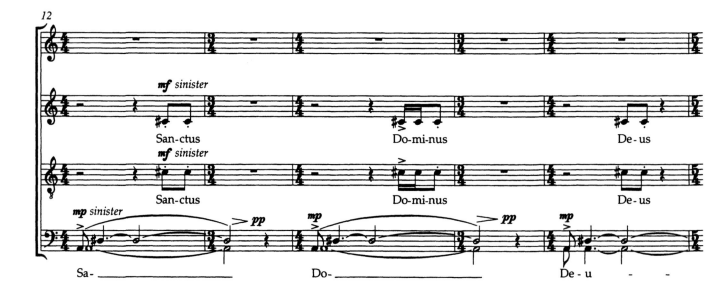

* pronounce *excelsis* 'ekselsis' throughout

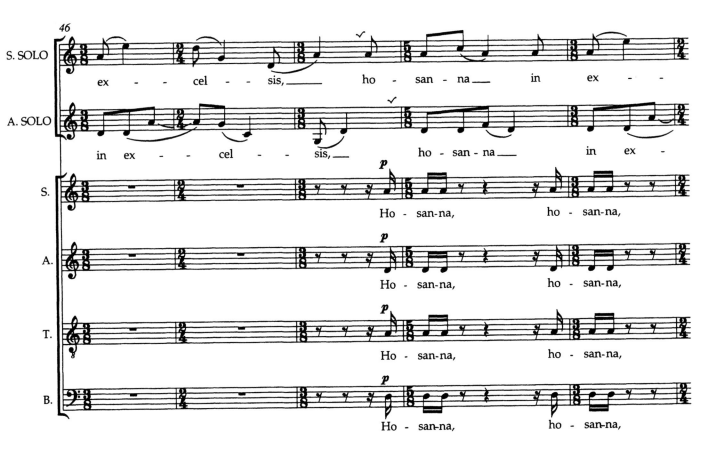

attacca

IV: benedictus

22

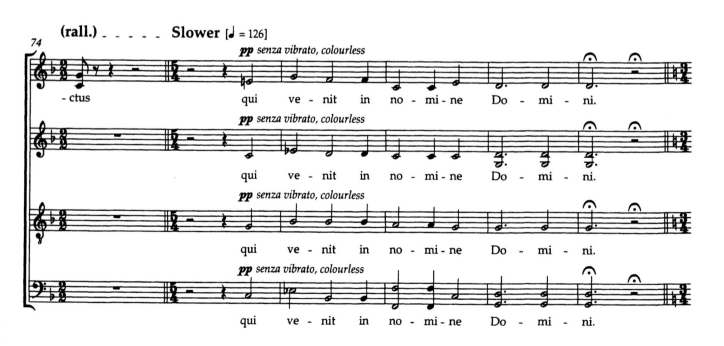

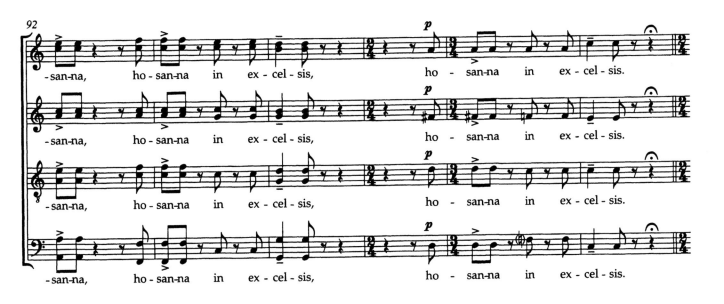

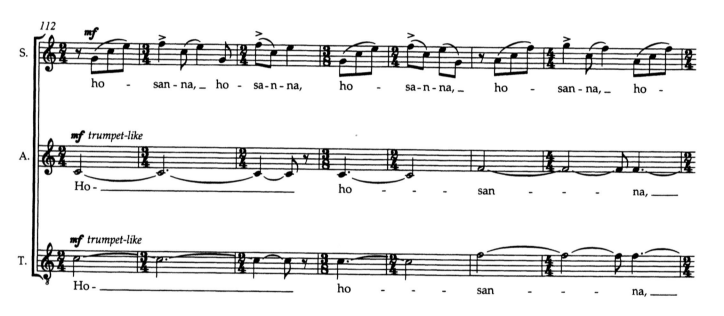

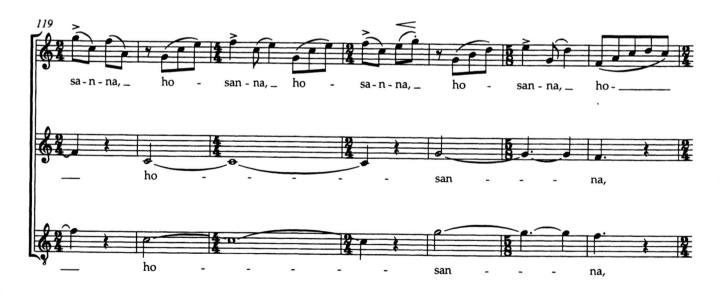

(senza rall.)

agnus dei

Sacrifices.

Some still perform them.

Want something special?

Kill a sheep.

Or a goat.

If you can afford it, an ox.

(Even a chicken will do)

It's a kind of bribe, really:

give the god something nice to eat,

and he may do what you ask him.

Sacrifices are dark, solemn affairs:

nothing sobers like a death.

Blood flows,

words and bodies flow

to another world.

Trance.

This moment,

now,

is a sacrifice:

we are the victims.

•

V: agnus dei

30

dona nobis pacem

Peace,

and the sanctity of all living things.

(Give us peace)

The dodo's waddle,

the praying-mantis of the Bushman –

they are gone forever.

(Give us peace)

Tiger, elephant, humming-bird and whale

must surely follow.

(Give us peace)

Peace means sharing what we have

while we still have it.

(Give us peace)

Peace means helping our neighbours,

not crushing them.

(Give us peace)

Peace means understanding.

It means balance.

It means love.

(Give us peace)

Above all, it means growing up.

(Give us peace)

We cry to our unknown god:

Give us peace,

before it is too late.

•

VI: dona nobis pacem

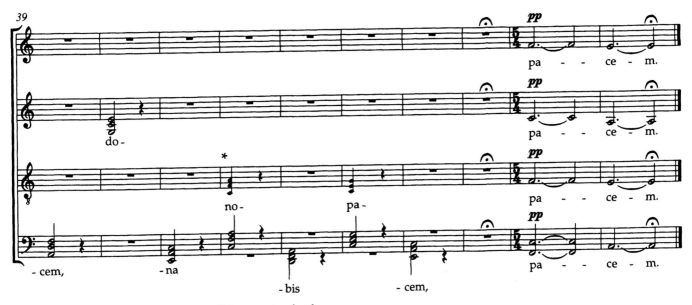

* These notes may be sung by the tenors if there are too few basses